· *Oxford Scientific Films* ·

DESERT WILDLIFE

Mike Linley

MALLARD PRESS

MALLARD PRESS
An Imprint of BDD Promotional Book Company, Inc.,
666 Fifth Avenue, New York, NY 10103.

Mallard Press and its accompanying design and logo
are trademarks of BDD Promotional Book Company, Inc.

CLB 2334
Copyright © 1989 Colour Library Books Ltd.
© 1989 Illustrations: Oxford Scientific Films Ltd,
Long Hanborough, England.
Color separation by Hong Kong Graphic Arts Ltd, Hong Kong.
First published in the United States of America
in 1989 by The Mallard Press.
Printed and bound in Italy by Fratelli Spada, SpA.
All rights reserved.
ISBN 0 792 45023 X

Contents

These pages: desert storms, when they do arrive, are often brief but spectacular, bringing some relief to the animals that live there.

Previous page: the frilled lizard has a startling display when alarmed.

1

Deserts of the World

Mention the word desert to someone and they immediately think of endless, rolling sand dunes completely devoid of plant and animal life. Well, some deserts are like this, but not all. Many deserts contain a surprising variety of life, although it may not be very obvious at first glance.

Any area with less than ten inches of rainfall per year can be called a desert, although most deserts receive far less than this. Deserts cover nearly a fifth (eight million square miles) of the earth's surface and are scattered throughout every continent, with the exception of Antartica.

Most occur to the north or south of the equator along the tropics of Cancer and Capricorn, both areas of dry winds and cool, offshore currents.

A desert may be sandy, stony or of bare rock, but they all have one thing in common – a climate in which temperatures can rocket to over 120°F and can plunge to below freezing at night. Many are constantly swept by dry winds, and if there is sand present this is often piled up to form dunes. Sand dunes may reach 600 or more feet in height and are constantly on the move, being nudged along by the wind. Some of the most impressive sand dunes are in the Sahara.

The Sahara Desert of North Africa is the biggest desert in the world, streching for some 3,000 miles from west to east and covering an area of some 3,500,000 square miles. Most of the interior of this desert receives less than an inch of rainfall a year. Any animal or plant living in the Sahara has to be well adapted to desert life in order to survive. Other deserts, like the one that covers much of central Australia, are less hostile environments and support a large variety of animal life.

Despite the lack of water, high daytime temperatures and low nighttime temperatures, the world's deserts play host to plants, mammals, birds, reptiles, amphibians, insects, spiders, and even fish and shrimps.

Facing page: even among the empty dunes of the desert, a gemsbok can find enough food to live on.

Below: not all deserts are empty rolling plains of sand. Desert areas in the State of Arizona are very rocky and support a variety of plant life.

2
A Shortage of Water

All life needs water in one form or another. Desert-living animals have two problems. First how to get water, and second how to keep within their bodies what little water they can obtain.

Plants usually have waxy skins and sharp spines to prevent water loss and deter herbivorous animals. Insects, spiders and scorpions obtain most of their moisture from the food they eat: plants in the case of many insects, or insects in the case of spiders and scorpions.

The little darkling beetle lives among the dunes of the Namib Desert in South West Africa. It emerges from the sand as dawn breaks, and positions itself on the very top of a dune. The beetle holds its head close to the ground and its body high in the air. The cold, moist air from the sea near the Namib causes a dew to form on the desert and on the body and legs of the beetle.

The thorny devil from the deserts of Australia has tiny grooves in its skin that channel dew and rain toward its mouth.

The droplets of water trickle down the insect and onto its mouthparts. The thorny devil, a small Australian lizard, has tiny grooves along its body that act in the same way, channeling the water to its mouth. Insects, scorpions and spiders have a hard, horny covering known as an exoskeleton that surrounds their body. It is very tough and waterproof, and prevents the insect from losing its body water. Reptiles have a similar covering in the form of scales, which are made of the same material, keratin, as our own fingernails. Like insects, reptiles obtain most of their moisture from their food: leaves in the case of the tortoises and some lizards, insects in the case of other lizards, and birds and small mammals in the case of snakes. They will, however, also drink water if it is available.

Among the mammals, the camel is legendary for its ability to survive long periods without drinking. It stores water in the form of fat in its hump, and even when this supply "dries up" it can survive losing up to a further twenty percent of its body liquids.

Above: the camel is well known for its ability to survive long periods without water. It stores water, in the form of fat, in its hump.

Left: the thrasher, like many small birds, can find moisture in some desert flowers.

Small mammals, such as the gerbil, spend the day in a burrow and emerge at night to feed on plant seeds and insects. They lose valuable moisture as they breathe, so they actually store dry seeds in their burrows which absorb this moisture. When they wake, they simply eat the seeds and recycle the moisture.

Birds have more of a problem with water in the desert. They cannot burrow or hide under rocks. One bird, the sand-grouse, has solved the problem of supplying water to its chicks in a very curious way. It flies many miles during the day in search of water and then sits in it. Special feathers on its chest absorb the water, and the bird then flies back to its chicks, which then suck the water from the feathers.

3
Problems of Heat

Many animals simply 'disappear' during the hottest part of the day, either under stones and into burrows or just below the sand's surface. Animals that don't burrow have to find other ways of keeping cool in the extreme heat of the desert.

Some reptiles, birds and mammals can lose heat by "panting", that is to say by breathing

Large ears allow many desert-living mammals to lose excess heat.

rapidly with the mouth open. As moisture evaporates from the lungs, mouth and tongue it cools down the tissues and blood.

This does, however, mean that the animal has to lose water in order to keep cool – a high

Above: larger mammals, like this coyote, can lose heat by panting.

Above right: many desert-living reptiles are very pale in color in order to reflect the heat of the sun.

price to pay in the desert. Mammals can also lose heat through the skin. Man sweats to keep cool in just the same way. The larger the area of exposed skin the more water can be evaporated for cooling. Some mammals, such as fennec foxes in Africa and jack rabbits in the deserts of North America, have extraordinarily large ears. The ears are well supplied with blood. As water evaporates from the skin, it cools down the blood, which is then circulated around the rest of the body, cooling that too. It works a little like the radiator in a car. The bigger the ears, the cooler the animal. An elephant's ears work in much the same way.

Colors also play an important role in temperature control. The paler the animal, the more sunlight, and thus heat, it reflects and the cooler the animal. A black animal in the desert would heat up very quickly because its body would absorb more heat.

At certain times of the day some animals actually need to absorb heat. Reptiles are only active when their bodies reach a certain temperature, almost that of our own. Below this temperature they become sluggish and slow-moving, so they have to spend some time in the morning "basking" in the sun. However, if they were simply to lie out in the open they would soon fall prey to predators.

The desert iguana of North America solves this problem by sitting with just its nose exposed from the sand. The blood in its head heats up and flows around its body and so, after a short time, it can emerge completely warmed up and ready to escape danger.

4
Desert Camouflage

Deserts are usually expanses of wide open space with few plants and rocks for animals to hide under. In order to avoid being seen, many animals use *camouflage*; that is to say, they are shaped or colored in such a way that they blend in with their background.

In the stony deserts of North America, grasshoppers are colored to match their background perfectly. In just the same way, the horned toad (it is in fact a lizard) is perfectly camouflaged. In certain deserts there are also tiny plants that have no leaves, only short, rounded stems that look just like stones.

Many insects are camouflaged to match the desert plants on which they live. The praying mantis lurks among the cacti ready to snap up any passing prey, and spiders wait near flowers

---

Facing page: a Namibian sidewinder lies in wait to seize any passing lizard or small mammal.

Below: the North-American horned toad blends in with its desert background very well. It is, in fact, not a toad but a lizard.

to catch bees and flies. Many butterflies are brightly colored on the upper surface of their wings, and perfectly camouflaged on the underside. In flight, when they would be visible anyway, they can readily identify each other. But while at rest, with their wings closed up, they match the ground perfectly. There are some butterflies that have two seasonal color forms: one to match their background during the "wet" season, if there is one, the other to match their background during the drought, when the earth is dry and bare.

Most desert mammals are pale brown or sandy in color, some in order to avoid being seen by *predators*, others to lie in wait unobserved for prey to come by.

One lizard, the desert chameleon from Namibia, can change its color to match almost any part of the desert. When it is walking across the sand it is a uniform pale color, when on a rocky plain it becomes mottled, and while on a plant it can turn green to match the leaves. This is the perfect solution to life in a varied environment.

5

Movement through the Sand

It is not easy for a man to walk up or down a sand dune, and many animals have exactly the same problem. The grains of sand have been eroded for years by the wind into tiny spheres which slide over each other very easily, making locomotion difficult.

Creatures such as the golden mole from the Namib can simply plough their way through the sand just below the surface in much the same way as other moles dig their way through the soil.

Golden moles are active only during the cool of the evening, and can move at high speed below the surface in search of burrowing insects and reptiles. They are completely blind and defenseless and, if exposed and placed on the surface, will disappear beneath the sand like a dolphin diving beneath the waves.

Many reptiles burrow through the loose sand. The amphisbaenian, a tiny, worm-like lizard moves just like an earthworm, squeezing its body like an accordion and then stretching it out. One burrowing skink from Egypt can move through the sand so quickly and easily that it is known as the sand-fish.

Some surface-dwelling lizards have modified feet to help them move over the loose surface. The American fringed-toed lizard is well named: along the side of each toe is a long fringe of scales that increases the surface area of its feet and so enables it to scuttle over the sand.

The Namibian sidewinder can move very quickly over soft sand in a series of rapid curving movements.

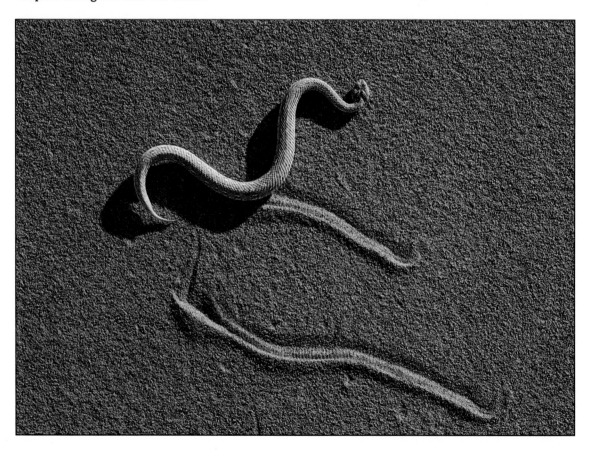

The Namibian *palmatogecko* even has webbed feet to enable it to dig out its burrow. Another reptile, the sidewinder, has developed a unique way of moving across the dunes. This snake moves in a series of S-bends, with only two parts of its body touching the ground at any one time. The tracks it leaves behind are unmistakable. Not surprisingly, this movement is known as sidewinding.

The biggest of all desert-adapted feet belong to the camel. The camel's foot is made up of only two large toes with a web of skin between them. As the camel applies its weight, the toes spread apart and the skin between them stretches and prevents the camel from sinking further into the sand.

Left: the little palmatogecko has webbed feet to enable it to dig burrows in the loose sand.

Below: many animals leave distinctive tracks behind in the desert sand.

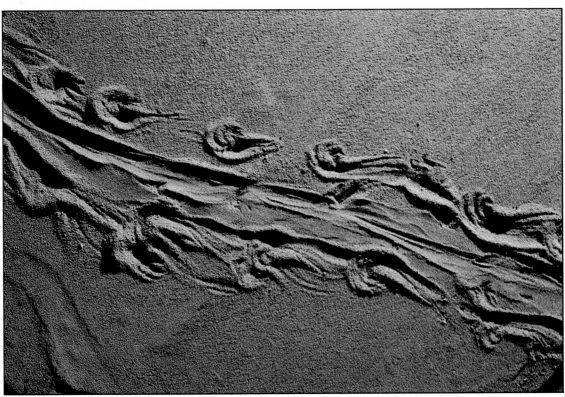

6
Desert Grazers

The *herbivores* of the desert, like those of any environment, form the vital link in the *food chain* between the basic plant-food sources and the higher *carnivorous* animals that, in turn, eat the herbivores. Wherever plants grow well there will be plenty of animals around to eat them.

In many deserts, green plants may not be available all year round, and those that are present may be protected by sharp spines or thick, waxy skins. Many desert creatures, therefore, feed on the tiny seeds that are blown around by the wind and lie, often for many years, ready to germinate when rains fall.

Above: plant-eating insects such as crickets are at the bottom of the food chain.

Left: large mammals, like the gemsbok, have to cover considerable distances in search of new vegetation.

The harvester ants of Arizona live in underground nests three or four metres below the surface. They emerge at dawn and dash about to scan the desert surface for tiny seeds. Those seeds that aren't eaten are stored in "granaries", hence their name.

Many species of small rodents, such as kangaroo rats in North America, and gerbils, jerboas and mice in Africa and Asia, feed mainly on plant seeds.

Desert tortoises will eat almost any plant they can find, but they have a particular passion for yellow flowers that only appear after heavy rain

Many desert species of birds also rely heavily on seed. Of all the desert creatures, birds probably have the most difficult time. They cannot hide away in burrows during the heat of the day and are unable to store large amounts of fat to see them through times of drought because it would impede their flight. But because they can fly they have the advantage of being able to cover huge distances in search of food and water.

True desert grazers often only have green leaves available as food for a limited period each year. Some, like the desert tortoise, cope by eating huge quantities while they can and living on their reserves or even *aestivating* when the food disappears.

Many desert-dwelling lizards are vegetarian: the chuckwalla of California and the mastigare of the Sahara eat leaves and, in particular, flowers. They can store large amounts of fat in their thick tails

The larger grazing mammals tend to live in groups or small herds and constantly roam the desert in search of fresh vegetation. Rainfall may be patchy and small areas of vegetation may spring up many miles apart. Many, like Dorca's gazelle, the addax and the gemsbok, never drink water, but obtain all the moisture they need from the plants they eat. In particularly bad years their numbers may fall, only to increase again when plenty of food is available.

7

Desert Hunters

Wherever herbivorous animals are found there will always be some sort of *carnivore* preying on them. The desert is home to a large number of predators. Lizards feed on ants and other insects. There are some lizards that feed exclusively on ants: in North America the horned toad sits at the entrance to the ants' nest and picks up hundreds during the course of a day. Across the other side of the world, in the deserts of Australia, the thorny devil lives in exactly the same way. Rattlesnakes feed on small mammals such as kangaroo rats. Rattlers belong to a group of snakes called pit vipers because they have a special pair of pits below their eyes. As well as using sight and smell to detect prey, they also sense the body heat of a mammal using these special pits. They can track down prey in complete darkness. One kangaroo rat may last the rattlesnake for a week or more, and it can then go without feeding for many months. Rattlesnakes in turn may fall prey to a desert-dwelling bird that spends much of its time on the ground. It shakes and batters the snake before swallowing it whole.

Among mammals, the little fennec fox of North Africa hunts insects and other smaller mammals. Its enormous ears not only help to keep it cool, but also act like two large radar dishes, amplifying the tiny noises made by insects and mammals below the sand's surface. The fox hears these sounds and then quickly digs away at the sand with its front feet before the prey has time to escape.

In southern Africa the meerkat, a small, mongoose-like animal, lives in large family

The little burrowing owl will eat lizards, snakes, small mammals and insects.

Snakes can survive for several weeks on a single, large meal.

*Above: the meerkat will eat almost any
small animal it can find.*

groups. It will catch and eat almost anything that moves, including insects, small snakes and scorpions, all of which it will eat, even the sting. Certain members of a group of meerkats will spend much of their day standing upright on their hind legs, on the lookout for birds of prey and other predators.

Should one member of the party see something, it emits a warning signal and the entire group disappear down their burrows in the flash of an eye. A few minutes later they will begin to peep out and cautiously emerge from their hiding places.

*Above: scorpions can obtain all the
moisture they need from the flesh of insects.*

*Facing page: A meerkat on guard in the
Kalahari Desert.*

8

Desert Scavengers

No Western film would be complete without the vultures circling in an empty sky over the scene of a recent "shoot-out" among the canyons.

When an animal dies in the desert, a whole host of creatures soon arrives to clear up the body. The vultures are usually the first on the scene, and will often follow a dying animal, waiting for it to drop. They have very light bodies and large, broad wings that enable them to ascend with the hot air rising from the desert. These "thermals" carry the birds hundreds of feet up into the skies. Vultures have excellent eyesight, enabling them to spot a dead or dying animal from some distance and swoop down to investigate. Other vultures circling a few miles away will see them drop and follow to investigate. Very soon dozens of vultures may descend onto a carcass.

While the vultures are busy feeding, much smaller animals are at work too. Tiny, flesh-eating carrion beetles are busy burying pieces of skin and flesh on which to lay their eggs. Ants, too, are removing tiny morsels to take back to their nest. Large lizards, called monitors in Africa and Asia and goannas in Australia, grip the flesh and turn their bodies to tear off chunks. Large mammals like jackals approach feeding vultures warily – they can be very aggressive, for food is often in short supply. The jackal may risk dashing in to remove a bone or a piece of meat, but will usually wait until the birds have finished before picking over the scraps. It is then that one of the largest of the scavengers moves in to clear up

Only the bleached bones and horns remain of this gemsbok; there is little that is wasted in the desert.

Above: hyenas will eat almost anything, even the tough, dried hide of a gemsbok.

Left: vultures are usually the first scavengers to find a dead or dying animal.

the leftovers. Hyenas will kill prey if they have to, but they feed mainly on carrion. They have very strong teeth and extremely powerful jaws, so powerful in fact that they can crush the thick leg bone of a large mammal to get at the marrow inside. They will also eat the bone itself for what little nourishment it contains.

Hyenas have very powerful digestive systems and everything, including fur, hooves, horns and bones, is swallowed. You can always identify a hyena scat because it consists of almost solid calcium from the bones it eats.

Nothing is wasted in the desert and a carcass, even one the size of a gembok's, disappears very quickly, usually within a day or two.

9
Life Under Ground

The only way many desert animals can survive in their environment is by spending the hottest part of the day under ground. Many emerge to forage and feed only in the cooler mornings and evenings, while some are completely nocturnal.

They may dig their own burrows or share those of another animal. Gophers are small, ground-living, squirrel-like mammals that live in the arid regions of North America. They live in large colonies and construct many underground tunnels and chambers. Many other animals share their home, so there is a "gopher tortoise", a "gopher frog" and a "gopher snake", plus an array of centipedes, scorpions and insects.

In the very sandy deserts of North Africa it is almost impossible to build a permanent burrow in the soft sand because it simply caves in. Many creatures just "swim" or wriggle through it. One spider, the white lady spider, has overcome this problem by using its web-silk to bind the sand grains together and make a tube. The entrance is a flap, covered so it is impossible to see. Should an insect walk by, the spider flings open

Above: the Australian holy cross toad stores large amounts of water in its bladder – a refreshing drink for a thirsty Aborigine.

Facing pages top: the little barking gecko emerges at night to hunt among the dunes of the Namib Desert.

the trap door, pounces on its prey and drags it down its burrow, closing the door behind it.

Many small, desert-dwelling mammals dig out tunnels with their front feet and kick the sand away with their hind feet. They may dig down eighteen inches or more to where the sand is more tightly compressed and may even be slightly damp. The majority of these mammals are nocturnal, but there is one group living in Africa and the Middle East that spends its entire life in underground tunnels, rarely, if ever, venturing onto the surface.

Naked mole-rats are strange-looking creatures with huge teeth, no eyes and hairless, pink skin. They dig their very complicated underground "villages" using their teeth, and feed on the roots and bulbs of plants. They also have a very curious "caste" system, with one 'queen' rat producing all the young, aided by several female "assistants".

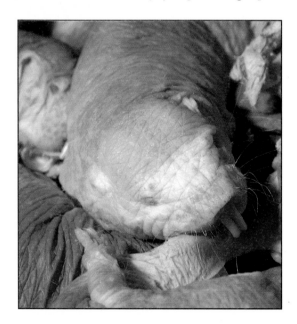

The naked mole-rat uses its large, chisel-like teeth to burrow through soil.

Desert burrowing frogs are some of the most remarkable of amphibians. They usually have some sand or a horny pad or ridge on their hind feet to enable them to shuffle backwards into the sandy soil. They may remain under ground for months, even years, waiting for the rains to come, when they will spring into action. One of them, the holy cross toad from the deserts of Australia, stores almost pure water in its bladder. Aborigines know how and where to find them and can dig them up, squeeze them and obtain a thirst-quenching drink that would not fill a thimble.

The gopher tortoise is often found sharing a gopher's burrow.

10

Desert Misfits

Spadefoot toads may spend a year or more underground before emerging at the onset of the rains.

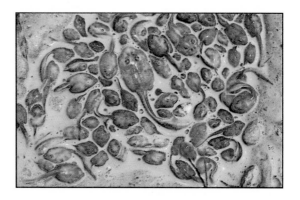

Above: spadefoot tadpoles can survive under conditions that would prove fatal to any other amphibian.

Facing page top: small, temporary pools are the breeding place of spadefoot toads and tadpole shrimps. These pools may only last a few days.

Facing page bottom: the eggs of the tadpole shrimp may lie dormant in the deepest sand for many years, but when it rains they will hatch and grow rapidly.

There are some animals, such as frogs and toads, shrimps and fishes, that thrive in deserts, but which one would not normally associate with heat and drought. In the deserts of North America and Mexico, for example, there are some dozen or so species of what can be described as "desert fish". They are, of course, confined to tiny desert springs and pools, but they exist under conditions that would kill most of their relatives. Some species, like the devil's hole pup fish, are confined to a single, tiny spring that can support, at most, about two or three hundred fish.

Spadefoot toads survive in the desert of Arizona not because they have a tough, waterproof skin, but because they have a thin, delicate skin that can let in tiny amounts of water if and when it is available. This toad spends ten months of the year buried underground using up its reserves of food and water, waiting for the rains. If the rains fail to arrive, the toads may spend up to two years buried beneath the soil. When the rains do fall the toads appear on the desert floor almost immediately, their emergence triggered by the pounding of falling rain. For them it is a race against time; they must spawn immediately if their tadpoles are to have any chance at all of surviving in the temporary desert pools. Once they have mated and spawned, the toads spend two or three weeks building up their fat and water reserves and then burrow down, only to emerge when the rains fall the following year. With luck their tadpoles will develop into tiny toads in less than three weeks, many of them becoming cannibalistic in order to survive.

Sharing their temporary pools of water are two types of shrimp: the fairy shrimp, so named because of the graceful way it moves through the water, and the tadpole shrimp, whose name describes its shape. Neither of these *crustaceans* can survive for long out of water, but within days of the rains they appear as if by magic. They do, in fact, survive in the form of minute eggs, left behind by the previous generation as the pools dried up. The eggs can survive for many years out of water and are blown about by the desert winds. A drop of water releases the tiny shrimp trapped inside.

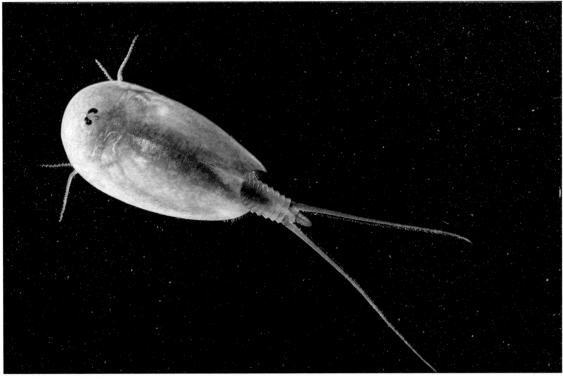

11
Migrants through the Desert

Many animals, especially birds, may have to cross vast expanses of desert in the course of their normal *migration* with the seasons.

Many northern-European birds migrate south to escape the rigors of winter. Shore birds like the sandpiper may breed around Europe, even as far north as the Arctic Circle, but during the winter they generally head for richer hunting grounds around Mauritania and Senegal, where the Sahara meets the sea.

Some of Europe's small, *insectivorous* birds, such as cuckoos, swallows and swifts, make their way through the Sahara en route to areas in Central Africa where they can catch the insects that are no longer available in the north. Many of these birds rely heavily on the numerous small oases dotted around the desert. Ground water may reach the soil's surface almost anywhere in the form of a small spring, and the Sahara desert is no exception. These oases transform the surrounding desert into a rich, fertile spot where the birds can drink and catch the insects that have set up residence there. Other, non-migratory species of birds may even live around the oasis permanently, having made their way there accidentally. In fact, an oasis may provide a home for a whole community of wildlife.

As well as birds, insects may cross the empty wastes of a desert. Hawkmoths, living off stored food and feeding when they can on flower nectar, are a common sight in parts of the Sahara, as are dragonflies heading northward, feeding on flies and other insects.

Perhaps the most famous of all migratory animals is the migratory locust of North Africa. This species lives in small numbers in and around the Sahara most of the year, but if the rain falls and the desert blooms then the numbers of locusts explodes, and swarms of up to 10,000 million insects may completely devour what little vegetation the desert has to offer and then head off to devastate the crops of the people who farm the surrounding savanna.

Facing page: the locust is the most famous desert migrant. Swarms of many hundreds of millions of these insects may appear after favorable weather conditions. Their eggs can survive for months underground.

Below: many North European birds, like this common sandpiper, migrate across the Sahara Desert on their way to and from wintering grounds.

12
Life at the Edge

Many animals, although not perfectly suited to life in the desert, may spend some time around the margins, venturing in and out as the weather and seasons permit. Many birds, such as ostriches and bustards, fall into this group. The ostrich is really a savanna bird, famed for its ability to eat and digest almost anything. It can survive for long periods without water, although it cannot live permanently in the desert. Huge groups of up to 200 birds may roam the plains, driven by the availability or absence of certain foods. Ostriches are great *opportunists,* and although they feed primarily on plant material, they won't hesitate to swallow small mammals, reptiles or, in fact, anything small enough to fit into their bill. An ostrich nest may contain two

---

Facing page top: lions, often thought of as hunters of the savanna, will venture into the Kalahari of Southern Africa in search of food.

Facing page bottom: ostriches can survive in the desert because of their ability to eat almost anything.

Below: the Nubian bustard nests in the more remote parts of the southern Sahara.

dozen or more eggs, laid by several females and looked after by one "mother". *Incubation* is not a problem in the desert heat – in fact the eggs often have to be kept shaded to keep them cool.

Bustards often use the desert as a safe place in which to lay their eggs and raise their chicks. The problems of raising a family in the desert are outweighed by the fact that, in general, the desert is home to few predators.

If rain should fall, the desert is tranformed very quickly from an empty, barren waste into a rich grazing ground for herbivorous mammals. Seeds that may have been lying dormant for many years in the sand burst into life. This rich supply of food attracts many animals such as gazelle, antelope and zebra into the area. But their venture into the desert will be short-lived. Within a few weeks of the rainfall the desert dries up again. The plants die, but leave more seeds in the ground waiting for the next downpour, which may take years to arrive. The *savanna* animals must move out of the desert back to the plains in order to survive. In some places the transition from savanna to desert may cover many miles while in others the desert may end at the bottom of a particular sand dune.

13
The Desert and Man

The desert must be one of the very few environments on earth that is not directly threatened by man's activities. It is also probably the only natural environment that's actually expanding rather than contracting due to the presence of man.

The southerly "growth" of the Sahara desert is well known. The Sahel, a region of scrub and bush around the edges of the Sahara is gradually disappearing, giving way to pure desert. In many areas it is possible to see dead trees half buried by the advancing sand dunes. The desertification of the Sahel is due, in part, to changes in the earth's weather patterns (which may be a result of the destruction of the rainforests) and also to man's activities. Many of the trees have been cut down by him to make charcoal, others have been stripped by his flocks of goats. The result is that the Sahara desert is "creeping" southwards.

These rock engravings in the Namib were made by bushmen who still roam this parched desert.

Man can often transform desert into rich, fertile land – simply by adding water.

Man may, in fact, create deserts himself by clearing away existing vegetation and planting single species of crops in their place. The soil gradually dries out and is literally blown away.

It's also very easy for man to turn a desert into lush, fertile farmland. All he needs to do is add water – lots of it. It is a very expensive process, but small areas of desert can be transformed. The Australian deserts are a case in point: by sinking bore-holes and irrigating the land, large areas are now suitable for grazing sheep.

The Australians have also witnessed an explosion in the numbers of red kangaroo because of the increase in available food.

Like the wildlife, there are also people who have learned to survive in the world's deserts. The Tuareg of the Sahara are a nomadic people who move around the Sahara Desert in search of grazing for their camels and goats, trading with other peoples living on the desert fringes.

The bushmen of the Kalahari are hunters and gatherers who can survive on minute quantities of water, most of which they obtain from the tubers of plants. The Bindibu of central Australia roam in small bands across the dusty, red deserts. Over the generations they have found a use for almost every plant and animal that they come across.

Deserts are so called because they appear "abandoned", empty of people, but there certainly are peoples who can and do exist in these, the most hostile of earth's environments.

Glossary

AESTIVATION Sleep to avoid hot weather.

CAMOUFLAGE The art of blending with a natural background.

CARNIVORE An animal that eats meat.

CRUSTACEANS A group of animals that includes crabs, shrimps, woodlice etc.

FOOD CHAIN The chain of nutrition of which plants form the base and flesh-eaters the upper levels.

HERBIVORE An animal that eats plants.

INCUBATION The heating process needed to hatch an egg.

INSECTIVORE An animal that eats insects.

MIGRATION Movement of animals from one area to another in response to weather or availability of food.

OPPORTUNIST An animal that makes full use of food or water as and when it is available.

PREDATOR An animal that kills and eats other animals.

SAVANNA An area of dry, open grassland.

Long-awaited rain brings forth a carpet of flowers whose seeds have lain dormant in the Kalahari for many years.